RSL 11+ Comprehension: *Vo*

These papers are accompanied by detailed, *teaching* mark schemes, designed to communicate the most important exam skills to students of all abilities. They provide a good preparation for any written comprehension test: the papers are structured in different ways, so that students will learn not to be daunted by an unfamiliar format.

The solution pages not only mark, but thoroughly teach the lessons from each exercise (these are things that I say frequently to my students). Some children will be able to use them independently, but they have been created with a supportive adult in mind: this pack will allow a parent to step confidently into the role of a tutor.

Please bear in mind that the example solutions are *no more than suggestions*. Very few of them claim to be the only possible approach. Read the discussion around each one if you want advice for assessing a different answer.

Although these papers have been designed carefully in response to the exams set by many schools in recent years, they cannot attempt to imitate every design of test, and they are not predictive. Sometimes a school sets another sort of exam: for example, a multiple-choice test. However, the skills of reading and analysis addressed in this pack will be a valuable preparation for any type of comprehension.

If you find these materials useful, you might be interested in reading about my *11 Plus Lifeline* service at **www.11pluslifeline.com**, which offers complete 11-plus preparation for all exams.

How To Use This Pack: Advice For Students

These materials can be used in different ways. For example, you may wish to answer some papers while reading the solutions, in order to understand how a comprehension exam works. However, most people will choose to write their answers then refer to the marking sheet.

When you are correcting your work, it is a good idea to take notes of any important points: this will help you to remember them. If your answer could be improved, it is often worth re-writing it with reference to the mark scheme.

These papers will be most useful if you complete them in order. Although each test and mark sheet can stand alone, used in sequence they will build up your skills steadily. There are eight papers, two of each type. The first of each pair provides answer spaces, while for the second you should use writing paper: this way you will learn to judge the best length for your answers.

The papers in this book have been designed for use without time limits, because they are focused on teaching each student to produce skilful, carefully written answers. When these skills have been acquired, it is usually a fairly simple matter to speed them up with the past papers available from most schools or through 11 Plus Lifeline. Timing problems are almost always caused by a lack of confidence with core techniques.

Essential advice for comprehension tests

- ✓ Read the passage; underline anything you do not fully understand.
- ✓ Read the questions.
- ✓ Return to your underlined phrases and work them out as best you can, now that you know the full context.
- ✓ Underline the key words in each question as you come to it (e.g. "why", "own words", "evidence", "lines 20-23").
- ✓ Look at the number of marks available for the question, and work out how your answer should be structured.
- ✓ Read the necessary paragraph(s) and underline any useful evidence. Keep underlining and quotations short, if possible (usually no more than six words).
- ✓ After writing your answer, check that you have answered every part of the question and have written enough for the number of marks.
- ✓ Check your English, and move on to the next question.

Never leave a blank space! If all else fails, make an educated guess. You might still get marks.

Finally, never cross out an answer unless you have already *completed* an improved one.

Also Available

11 Plus Lifeline (printable materials for all 11+ subjects): **www.11pluslifeline.com**
RSL 11+ Comprehension: Volume 2
RSL 11+ Maths
RSL 8+ Comprehension (8+ to 10+ levels)
RSL 13+ Comprehension
GCSE Maths by RSL, Higher Level (9-1), Non-Calculator
GCSE Spanish by RSL
GCSE French by RSL
GCSE German by RSL (due September 2019)

We are a family business in a competitive marketplace. We want to improve and expand our range, providing even better products for our customers, including families who may not wish to purchase long courses of private tuition. If you have any feedback, please let me know! My email address is **robert@rsleducational.co.uk**.

If you like this book, please tell your friends and write a review on Amazon!

Contents

I recommend **cutting out the comprehension passages along the dotted lines**, so that they are always in view while answering the questions. This will encourage students to refer back to the text on every possible occasion and to write focused, properly evidenced answers.

RSL 11+ Comprehension: Volume 1 (2nd edition)
By Robert Lomax
Published by RSL Educational Ltd
Copyright © RSL Educational Ltd 2019

Company 10793232 - VAT 252515326 - Willey Lodge, Presteigne, LD8 2NB - Registered in England & Wales

Blank Page

Paper 1: *Jane Eyre*

Type A: *Standard Level*

Jane Eyre, a young orphan, lives with her aunt, Mrs Reed, and the Reed children. She has been reading by the library window, behind the curtain. John Reed (who is 14) has ordered her to come out.

All at once, without speaking, he struck suddenly and strongly. I tottered, and on regaining my balance retired back a step or two from his chair.

"That is for your rudeness in answering Mama a while ago," said he, "and for your sneaking way of getting behind curtains, and for the look you had in your eyes two
5   minutes ago, you rat!"

Accustomed to John Reed's abuse, I never had an idea of replying to it; my care was how to endure the blow which would certainly follow the insult.

"What were you doing behind the curtain?" he asked.

"I was reading."

10   "Show the book."

I returned to the window and fetched it.

"You have no business to take our books; you are a dependent, Mama says; you have no money; your father left you none; you ought to beg, and not to live here with gentlemen's children like us, and eat the same meals we do, and wear clothes at our
15   mama's expense. Now, I'll teach you to rummage my bookshelves: for they are mine; all the house belongs to me, or will do in a few years. Go and stand by the door, out of the way of the mirror and the windows."

I did so, not at first aware what was his intention; but when I saw him lift and poise the book and stand about to hurl it, I instinctively jumped aside with a cry of alarm:
20   not soon enough, however; the volume was flung, it hit me, and I fell, striking my head against the door and cutting it. The cut bled, the pain was sharp: my terror had passed its high point; other feelings followed.

"Wicked and cruel boy!" I said. "You are like a murderer—you are like a slave-driver—you are like the Roman emperors!"

25   "What! what!" he cried. "Did she say that to me? Did you hear her, Eliza and Georgiana? Won't I tell Mama? but first—"

He ran headlong at me: I felt him grasp my hair and my shoulder. I really saw in him a tyrant, a murderer. I felt a drop or two of blood from my head trickle down my neck.

Adapted from *Jane Eyre,* by Charlotte Brontë

1.   Why does Jane "retire back a step or two" from John's chair?   **(1)**

       ....

       ....

2.   Explain John's reasons for hitting Jane, as given in lines 3-5. Use your own
       words.   **(3)**

       ....

       ....

       ....

3.   What do you think the word "dependent" means (line 12)?   **(2)**

       ....

       ....

       ....

4.   "All the house belongs to me, or will do in a few years." What does John mean
       by this?   **(3)**

       ....

       ....

       ....

       ....

5. What are your impressions of Jane's character? Support your answer with evidence from the passage. **(4)**

....

....

....

....

....

....

....

6. In your opinion, could Jane and John become friends? Give evidence to support your answer. **(5)**

....

....

....

....

....

....

....

7. Jane accuses John of being like "a murderer", "a slave driver" and "the Roman emperors". In your opinion, which of these best describes him? Explain your answer. **(2)**

....

....

....

8. Imagine that John's mother comes in. Continue the story (write about 100-150 words). Try to use the same style as the passage. **(5)**

....

....

....

....

....

....

....

....

....

....

....

....

....

....

....

TOTAL MARKS: 25

Jane Eyre – **Solutions**

This test has no surprises and reflects the standard level of 11-plus exams as set by the ISEB and used by many independent schools. However, it requires clear explanations and the use of carefully selected evidence. Because the passage is from an old book, it also includes some moderately challenging language.

The answer spaces should help you judge how much to write.

> **1.   Why does Jane "retire back a step or two" from John's chair?   (1)**
>
> She does this because he has "struck" her.

This is a one-mark question, so only needs a simple answer – although the answer should be a complete sentence. The word "retire" is difficult, but you can work out its meaning from the other information.

An alternative answer might be:

> She does this to avoid being hit again.

It is important to realise, particularly in comprehensions where you are given limited space for each answer, that **you do not need to repeat the question**. "She does this to avoid being hit again" is just as much a sentence as "Jane 'retires back a step or two from John's chair' to avoid being hit again", but it is a great deal simpler to write.

> **2.   Explain John's reasons for hitting Jane, as given in lines 3-5. Use your own words.   (3)**
>
> He says that she has insulted his mother, that she hides from him behind curtains, and that she made a rude face two minutes before.

There are three main points here, and you need to find all of them for three marks. It helps to underline the different points in the passage before answering this sort of question.

"Own words" tells you not to repeat words from the passage if you can avoid it: you must **demonstrate understanding through your ability to rephrase**. The example repeats "behind curtains" – this is difficult to say in another way – but makes up for this by saying "she hides from him", which shows that the meaning is understood.

> **3.   What do you think the word "dependent" means (line 12)?**   **(2)**
>
> This means that she needs other people to feed her and give her clothes.

The main point is that she is someone who depends (relies) on other people, but because there are two marks for this, you should give some more information.

Always re-read the whole paragraph before answering a question like this: clues such as "eat the same meals we do" and "wear clothes at our mamma's expense" will help you to work out the answer.

> **4.   "All the house belongs to me, or will do in a few years." What does John mean by this?**   **(3)**
>
> John means that in the future he will own the house, because it will become his when he is an adult, or maybe after his mother dies. Because of this, he treats it as though it is already his: he gets to choose what happens there.

This is a tricky question, because there are two parts to the quotation. If you can explain why the house "will" be his, that is worth two marks. To get the other mark, you must explain the first part as well: the word "belongs", which refers to the present rather than the future.

As a rule, **when a question asks you to explain a quotation, make sure that you explain every part of it**.

> **5.   What are your impressions of Jane's character? Support your answer with evidence from the passage.**   **(4)**
>
> Jane does not like to argue: when John hits her, she does not have "an idea of replying". She is good at entertaining herself, because she has been "reading" quietly, by herself. She is brave, because very soon after falling, her "terror" calms down. She is knowledgeable, because she compares John to "the Roman emperors".

If you get a four-mark "impressions of character" question like this, you do not know whether the examiner wants two points and two pieces of evidence (like for many four-mark questions), or four separate points (because it would be strange to sum up a character with only two comments). If you think this is unfair – well, I agree. At any rate, it's safest to make four points if you can, with brief evidence for each.

Having said this, I would give four marks for two clear points with evidence, if it were down to me.

The best kind of evidence is a short quotation.

There are **two common mistakes** that people make in these questions.

- Firstly, people write things that are not exactly about *personality*. For example, they say that Jane is younger than John.

- Secondly, they write two or more points that are not completely different.

Here is an example of a **<u>poor</u>** answer to the question, showing both these faults. It would only achieve one or two marks:

> *Jane is not easily scared, because she only feels "terror" for a short time. She is also brave, because she stands up to John. She shows courage when she shouts that he is a "cruel boy". Finally, I think Jane is quite a small person, because she can hide behind a curtain.*

A good way to answer questions like this is to underline various things that the character says, thinks or does, then ask yourself what sort of person might do that.

Bear in mind that you do not necessarily need a single word for the concept. Imagine that you want to say "shy", but have forgotten the word: you could also write "does not like to be with people".

> **6. In your opinion, could Jane and John become friends? Give evidence to support your answer.** **(5)**
>
> I think they would be unlikely to become friends, because their characters are so different. When Jane has to defend herself she just uses words, saying "you are like a murderer", but John is violent and hits her "without speaking". John is a coward, because he wants to get help ("won't I tell mamma?"), but Jane is very brave: she wants to "endure the blow".

Don't forget to give **a clear answer to the question** ("Could [they] become friends?"). This is worth one mark. Then you need to make a number of clear points in support of your answer. Use short quotations as evidence where possible.

If you only write about one character, you will lose marks.

It is possible to argue that they *could* be friends, but you might have trouble finding enough points to back up your opinion.

---

7. **Jane accuses John of being like "a murderer", "a slave driver" and "the Roman emperors". In your opinion, which of these best describes him? Explain your answer.** (2)

John is best described as being like "a slave driver", because he gives Jane orders such as "show the book", and he thinks that she is a less important person with fewer rights than him ("you are a dependent").

or

John is like a "Roman emperor" because he is very proud ("Did you say that to me?") and because Jane sees him as "a tyrant".

or

She is right to compare him to "a murderer", because he is violent ("he struck … strongly"), and just hurting her doesn't seem to be enough: he does it several times ("it hit me"; "I felt him grasp my hair"), without caring how much he harms her.

Any choice is possible, as long as it is explained. A good explanation that makes two different points, or a single point that is fully developed, will achieve two marks.

Quotations are not requested, but your answer cannot be properly "explained" without some reference to the passage.

8. **Imagine that John's mother comes in. Continue the story (write about 100-150 words). Try to use the same style as the passage.** (5)

This is how Charlotte Brontë continues:

I don't very well know what I did with my hands, but he called me "Rat! Rat!" and bellowed out aloud. Aid was near him: Eliza and Georgiana had run for Mrs Reed, who was upstairs; she now came upon the scene, followed by Bessie and her maid Abbot.

We were parted: I heard the words, "Dear! Dear! What a fury to fly at Master John!"

"Did anybody ever see such a picture of passion?"

Then Mrs Reed ordered, "Take her away to the red room, and lock her in there." Four hands were immediately laid upon me, and I was borne upstairs.

Of course, any reasonable plot choice is fine. The important thing is to write in a way that continues the style of the passage, and to paint the scene effectively.

In order to show off your skills as a writer, it might even be wise to use **more description than Brontë herself does!**

Here is another possibility:

> His hands were beating, tearing … I held my eyes shut, and I could see the candle-light pulsating through my eyelids. I felt more tiredness than pain, but I could taste blood.
>
> Then the blows stopped, and I felt as though I was falling, still falling, sinking deep into the carpet. If I could just sleep here, now …
>
> A great *slap* made me start – but I felt nothing. As I opened my eyes, I saw John's toes dangling above the carpet. The enormous figure of Mrs Reed stared down at him past the tip of her chin. She held him by the collar, at arm's length. Her eye flicked my way, and for a moment I thought I saw a smile.

If you make too many grammatical or spelling errors when answering a creative writing question, you are likely to lose marks. Be very careful to avoid basic mistakes, such as not using the first person ("I") like the passage does, or moving the action into the present.

Also, be sure to do whatever you are asked (here, to have John's mother enter).

You may wish to use some of the following techniques: **onomatopoeia** ("quack"); **simile** ("he yawned like a feeding whale"); **various senses** (the usual five are sight, hearing, touch, smell and taste); **alliteration** ("a slap made me start"); **metaphor** ("the clouds were a messy blanket stretched above him"); **short/long sentences**; **dialogue** (speech).

Of course, there are many other possibilities. Don't let any single technique dominate your answer.

If your answer shows some imagination and skill, makes sense as a development of the story, and is written in correct (or almost correct) English, it will achieve full marks.

> For free 11-plus creative writing advice, see **www.rsleducational.co.uk/11-plus-creative-writing/**

END

Paper 2:

FLYING MACHINE SOARS 3 MILES IN TEETH OF HIGH WIND OVER SAND HILLS AND WAVES AT KITTY HAWK ON CAROLINA COAST

Type A: Standard Level

The American brothers Orville and Wilbur Wright made the first sustained aeroplane flight on the 17th of December, 1903. This newspaper article is from the following day.

The problem of aerial navigation without the use of a balloon has been solved at last.

Over the sand hills of the North Carolina coast yesterday, near Kitty Hawk, two Ohio men proved that they could soar through the air in a flying machine of their own construction, with the power to steer it and speed it at will. This, too, in the face of a
5   wind blowing at the confirmed velocity of twenty-one miles an hour.

Like a monster bird, the invention hovered above the breakers and circled over the rolling sand hills at the command of its navigator and, after soaring for three miles, it gracefully descended to earth again and rested lightly upon the spot selected by the man in the car as a suitable landing place.

10 While the United States government has been spending thousands of dollars in an effort to make practicable the ideas of Professor Langley of the Smithsonian Institute, Wilbur and Orville Wright, two brothers, natives of Dayton, Ohio, have quietly, even secretly, perfected their invention, and put it to a successful test.

They are not yet ready that the world should know the methods they have adopted in
15 conquering the air, but the *Virginian-Pilot* is able to state authentically the nature of their invention.

Start Was Success

Wilbur Wright, the chief inventor of the machine, sat in the operator's car and when all was ready his brother unfastened the catch which held the invention at the top of the slope.

20 The big box began to move slowly at first, acquiring velocity as it went, and when half way down the hundred feet the engine was started.

The propeller in the rear immediately began to revolve at a high rate of speed, and when the end of the incline was reached the machine shot out into space without a perceptible fall.

25 By this time the elevating propeller was also in motion, and, keeping its altitude, the machine slowly began to go higher and higher until it finally soared sixty feet above the ground.

Maintaining this height by the action of the under wheel, the navigator increased the revolutions of the rear propeller, and the forward speed of the huge affair increased 30 until a velocity of eight miles an hour was attained.

Coast Folk Amazed

The little crowd of fisher folk and coast guards, who have been watching the construction of the machine with unconcerned curiosity since September 1st, were amazed.

They endeavoured to race over the sand and keep up with the thing of the air, but it 35 soon distanced them and continued its flight alone, except for the man in the car.

Steadily it pursued its way, first tacking to port, then to starboard, and then driving straight ahead.

"It is a success," declared Orville Wright to the crowd on the beach after the first mile had been covered.

40 But the inventor waited. Not until he had accomplished three miles, putting the machine through all sorts of manoeuvres *en route*, was he satisfied.

Then he selected a suitable place to land, and, gracefully circling, drew his invention slowly to the earth, where it settled, like some big bird, in the chosen spot.

"Eureka!" he cried, as did the alchemist of old.

Adapted from the *Virginian Pilot* newspaper

1.   What is the "problem" referred to in line 1? Use your own words as far as possible.   **(2)**

2.   **(a)** According to the newspaper article, how fast was the wind?   **(1)**

        (b) Why, in the view of the journalist (writer), is this information important?   **(2)**

3.   Briefly explain the comparison between the United States government and the Wright brothers in lines 10-13.   **(3)**

4.   What is the name of the aeroplane's pilot?   **(1)**

5.   Using your own words, explain how the aircraft is made to take off.   **(3)**

6.   Giving evidence from the text, explain how the journalist makes this article exciting.   **(4)**

7.   **(a)** The article never uses the words "aeroplane" or "plane". List two other names for the machine, used instead of these.   **(2)**

        (b) Why do you think the word "aeroplane" is not used?   **(1)**

8.   Throughout the passage the writer compares the "flying machine" to a bird. What do these comparisons suggest about the aeroplane and its flight? Give evidence to support your points.   **(6)**

TOTAL MARKS: 25

FLYING MACHINE SOARS 3 MILES IN TEETH OF HIGH WIND OVER SAND HILLS AND WAVES AT KITTY HAWK ON CAROLINA COAST – Solutions

This comprehension has a similar structure to the previous one and its difficulty is comparable. However, it places more emphasis on understanding and explaining the meaning of the text and the ways in which it is effective. There is less room for using your own imagination.

There are no spaces for you to write in, which means that you will need to decide on a sensible length for each answer while using your own lined paper.

> **1. What is the "problem" referred to in line 1? Use your own words as far as possible. (2)**
>
> It is the problem of finding a way to fly through the air, without being lifted by a balloon.

"Use your own words" means that **you should avoid using words from the text**; the question says "as far as possible" because it is difficult to find a good alternative to "balloon", and you are not expected to. The main challenge is to explain "aerial navigation" clearly. Anything to do with flying is likely to be fine.

Ideally, you should also show that you understand "without the use of". How might a balloon have been "used" to solve this problem before?

If you answer the question clearly, but your response too closely copies the text, you will get one mark.

> **2. (a) According to the newspaper article, how fast was the wind? (1)**
>
> It had a speed of "twenty-one miles an hour".

To answer this, you need to know that "velocity" means speed (in a particular direction), though you are free to use either word (or neither) in your response.

> **(b) Why, in the view of the journalist (writer), is this information important?**
> **(2)**
>
> The plane is flying "in the face of" (against) this strong wind, but can still travel easily and be controlled by the pilot. This shows how impressive and well-made the "flying machine" is.

You need to base your answer on the rest of the sentence ('in the face of'), and show that you clearly understand why this matters.

When you have a two-mark question like this one, try to give the marker **two things to tick**: this is why the example has a second sentence. However, they may be generous and give you a second mark if you clearly understand the main point, even without making a second one.

> **3.**   **Briefly explain the comparison between the United States government and the Wright brothers in lines 10-13.**   **(3)**
>
> The U.S. government has spent huge amounts of money trying to invent a flying machine of this sort, yet the brothers have "quietly" made their "invention" fly, by themselves.

You need to work out that the government has been trying to invent an aeroplane. The passage doesn't actually say this, so the question is quite sneaky. Just working this out is worth one mark.

The other two marks are for clearly explaining the contrast between what the government has been *trying* to do, and what the Wright brothers have *actually* done themselves.

You should probably mention that the government has spent a lot of money, whereas the brothers have presumably done it with far less.

> **4.**   **What is the name of the aeroplane's pilot?**   **(1)**
>
> He is called Wilbur Wright.

This comes from line 17. The challenge is to recognise that "sat in the operator's car" means that Wilbur is in the cockpit (cabin) of the aircraft. You could also work it out from line 38, where Orville Wright is said to be "on the beach".

Notice how you can avoid repeating the question, which you may not have time to copy in an exam: "He is called Wilbur Wright" is a full sentence (it has a subject, "he", and a verb), so you do **not** need to write "The name of the aeroplane's pilot is Wilbur Wright."

> **5.   Using your own words, explain how the aircraft is made to take off.   (3)**
>
> Orville releases the aircraft on a hill. It speeds up as it rolls, and after fifty feet the engine is switched on. The propeller behind the plane spins rapidly, and at the bottom of the slope there is a ledge or cliff, over which the aircraft shoots into the air without a bump.

You need to mention that it runs down a hill, that the engine is started as it rolls, and that it flies into the air at the bottom of the slope. Be careful to use your own words.

The example makes some other points from the text (for example that the plane seems to launch from a cliff of some kind – "without a perceptible fall", lines 23-24), in order to be thorough, and therefore safe.

> **6.   Giving evidence from the text, explain how the journalist makes this article exciting.   (4)**
>
> Firstly, the writer uses exciting words and phrases like "soar" and "shot out". These show the machine's power, so that you can imagine what it was like to see a "big box" actually lift from the ground and fly away for the first time. Secondly, they talk about the "coast folk" who have been "watching the construction" with interest but without any surprise. These people are "amazed" by the flight, which helps to show how spectacular it seemed to those who were there. The image of these people chasing the aeroplane in a "race" along the beach is very dramatic.

The question doesn't tell you how many points to make, but you are probably already getting the hang of this: because it asks for "evidence", you can be fairly confident that there is a mark for each explained point, and a mark for providing a good quote to back it up. Therefore you need to make two points.

My advice for an exam is to leave space, and come back at the end of the test to make a third point if you have time, just to be certain.

Be careful: **your evidence should clearly back up your ideas**, and **your points must be very different from each other**.

The last sentence in the example is probably unnecessary for the marks. It is included to make sure that the second point is completely explained: so there can be no doubt that this is about the flight being "exciting".

There is another awkward thing about this question: if you have not read ahead, you might accidentally use ideas that you would rather have saved for Question 8. This is the fault of the person who wrote the test (whoever that was), so you *shouldn't* lose marks for repeating a similar point later – but to be safe, it is best to avoid bird images in this answer if you can.

> **7.   (a) The article never uses the words "aeroplane" or "plane". List two other names for the machine, used instead of these.**   **(2)**
>
> "big box"
> "flying machine"

This asks for "names for the machine" used **instead of** "plane", so a *comparison* such as "like a monster bird" would only be worth half a mark.

"List", like "write down", tells you not to worry about full sentences.

There is nothing wrong with using phrases that you have already quoted in other answers.

> **(b) Why do you think the word "aeroplane" is not used?**   **(1)**
> This is probably because the word had not been invented yet.

(In fact, the word did exist, but it referred to the wing, not the entire aircraft. You are obviously not expected to know this.)

Any sensible answer will do, but it would be incorrect to say that this machine is in some way *not actually an aeroplane*: the introduction uses the term, and so does Question 4.

> **8.** **Throughout the passage the writer compares the "flying machine" to a bird. What do these comparisons suggest about the aeroplane and its flight? Give evidence to support your points.** **(6)**
>
> The journalist is impressed by how the aircraft is comfortable both in the air and on the ground. At the end of the "soaring" flight it "settled, like some big bird", the simile suggesting the ease and security with which it lands. What's more, the landing is elsewhere described as "rest[ing] lightly", which implies that it is only visiting the earth to catch its breath, and could take off again at any time: this is not a one-off event, because flying is here to stay. On the other hand, this graceful elegance goes side by side with something more sinister. The plane is a "monster bird", terrible in its power, strangely horrifying as it breaks the limits of what people previously thought they could do. It achieves something that would once have been put down to magic.

The challenge of this question is that there are not three *direct* bird quotes in the text. Aside from "like some big bird" and "monster bird", you need to track down moments when it is **described in a similar way to a bird** – for example when it is "soaring".

You should aim to make three points, with evidence for each of them. However, markers ought to be fairly flexible. If you develop two points fully (ideally with some extra evidence, such as the quotes for flying and landing in the first point above), you may well get six marks. The main thing is to offer six different things to tick.

END

Paper 3: *The Trial*

Type B: Intermediate Level

The Knave of Hearts is on trial for stealing some tarts. The King of Hearts is the judge, and the jury will decide whether the Knave is guilty. Alice has just now been called to give evidence, as a witness.

"Here!" cried Alice, quite forgetting in the flurry of the moment how large she had grown in the last few minutes, and she jumped up in such a hurry that she tipped over the jury-box with the edge of her skirt, upsetting all the jurymen on to the heads of the crowd below, and there they lay sprawling about, reminding her very much of a globe
5   of goldfish she had accidentally upset the week before.

"Oh, I beg your pardon!" she exclaimed in a tone of great dismay, and began picking them up again as quickly as she could, for the accident of the goldfish kept running in her head, and she had a vague sort of idea that they must be collected at once and put back into the jury-box, or they would die.

10 "The trial cannot proceed," said the King in a very grave voice, "until all the jurymen are back in their proper places—all," he repeated with great emphasis, looking hard at Alice as he said so.

Alice looked at the jury-box, and saw that, in her haste, she had put the Lizard in head downwards, and the poor little thing was waving its tail about in a melancholy way,
15 being quite unable to move. She soon got it out again, and put it right; "not that it signifies much," she said to herself; "I should think it would be quite as much use in the trial one way up as the other."

As soon as the jury had a little recovered from the shock of being upset, and their slates and pencils had been found and handed back to them, they set to work very
20 diligently to write out a history of the accident, all except the Lizard, who seemed too much overcome to do anything but sit with its mouth open, gazing up into the roof of the court.

"What do you know about this business?" the King said to Alice.

"Nothing," said Alice.

25 "Nothing whatever?" persisted the King.

"Nothing whatever," said Alice.

"That's very important," the King said, turning to the jury. They were just beginning to write this down on their slates, when the White Rabbit interrupted:

30   "Unimportant, your Majesty means, of course," he said in a very respectful tone, but frowning and making faces at him as he spoke.

"Unimportant, of course, I meant," the King hastily said, and went on to himself in an undertone, "important—unimportant—unimportant—important—" as if he were trying which word sounded best.

35   Some of the jury wrote down "important," and some "unimportant." Alice could see this, as she was near enough to look over their slates; "but it doesn't matter a bit," she thought to herself.

At this moment the King, who had been for some time busily writing in his note-book, cackled out "Silence!" and read out from his book, "Rule Forty-two. All persons more than a mile high to leave the court."

40   Everybody looked at Alice.

From *Alice's Adventures in Wonderland,* by Lewis Carroll

1.   Give the meanings of the following words, as they are used in the text:

(a) Melancholy (line 14)   ……*very*…………………………………………… **(1)**

(b) Overcome (line 21)   ……………………………………………………… **(1)**

(c) Cackled (line 38)   ……………………………………………………… **(1)**

2.   Basing your answer on the information in lines 2-9, explain why Alice is
        worried that the jury might "die".   **(4)**

…………………………………………………………………………………………

…………………………………………………………………………………………

…………………………………………………………………………………………

…………………………………………………………………………………………

…………………………………………………………………………………………

3.   Why does Alice think that the Lizard "would be quite as much use in the trial
        one way up as another" (lines 16-17)?   **(2)**

…………………………………………………………………………………………

…………………………………………………………………………………………

…………………………………………………………………………………………

4.   "Upset" in line 18 has two possible meanings. What are they?   **(2)**

(i)   …………………………………………………………………………………

(ii)   …………………………………………………………………………………

5.   Why in lines 29-30 does the White Rabbit speak "in a very respectful tone"
        while "frowning and making faces"?   **(3)**

…………………………………………………………………………………………

…………………………………………………………………………………………

…………………………………………………………………………………………

…………………………………………………………………………………………

6. What do lines 31-33 suggest about the King's personality? **(3)**

....

....

....

....

....

7. Why does Alice think that "it doesn't matter a bit" that "some of the jury wrote down 'important' and some 'unimportant'" (line 35)? **(2)**

....

....

....

8. In the end, the jury will need to decide whether the Knave of Hearts is guilty. Basing your answer on evidence from the text, how much would you trust their decision? **(6)**

....

....

....

....

....

....

....

....

9.   **(a)** Write down, from four different sentences in the passage:

(i)   an adjective   …………………………………………………………………..

(ii)   a noun   …………………………………………………………………..

(iii)   a verb   …………………………………………………………………..

(iv)   an adverb   ……………………………………………………….....   **(2)**

         (b) Invent a single sentence that uses all four words in **(a)** correctly.   **(2)**

………………………………………………………………………………………………..

………………………………………………………………………………………………..

………………………………………………………………………………………………..

10.   What does Alice think about this trial and the people involved in it? Support
         your answer with evidence.   **(6)**

………………………………………………………………………………………………..

………………………………………………………………………………………………..

………………………………………………………………………………………………..

………………………………………………………………………………………………..

………………………………………………………………………………………………..

………………………………………………………………………………………………..

………………………………………………………………………………………………..

………………………………………………………………………………………………..

………………………………………………………………………………………………..

………………………………………………………………………………………………..

TOTAL MARKS: 35

The Trial – Solutions

The questions in this comprehension are not too difficult, but they do require a significant number of short, clear answers. In the previous papers, you could lose a mark on each answer and still get a decent score overall. If you did that here, you would not do well! Therefore, this is all about attention to detail.

---

1.   Give the meanings of the following words, as they are used in the text:
(a) Melancholy (line 14)   **(1)**
Sad
(b) Overcome (line 21)   **(1)**
Overwhelmed / stunned / distressed
(c) Cackled (line 38)   **(1)**
Called out in a dry, croaky voice

The limited answer space should make it clear that full sentences are not required.

Some markers will give a half mark to an answer that is reasonable, but not entirely correct.

Be careful to explain the meanings of the words **as used in the text**. In other contexts "cackled" might mean "laughed", and "overcome" might be a verb meaning "defeated" or "conquered", but these are evidently not their meanings here.

---

2.   Basing your answer on the information in lines 2-9, explain why Alice is worried that the jury might "die".   **(4)**
Alice has knocked over the "jury-box", and the jury's helplessness reminds her of a goldfish bowl she overturned recently. Because the goldfish would have died if left out of the water, Alice gets confused for a moment and thinks that the jury will also die if they are not put back in their box.

Because this question tells you where to look for information, you can tell that it wants you to be thorough: you need to include all the main points that are relevant.

Although this question doesn't need you to write everything in your own words, **you will not get marks if you quote a large part of the section without showing that you understand it**.

The main points are included in the example above; take away a mark for each one that you have missed.

> **3.** **Why does Alice think that the Lizard "would be quite as much use in the trial one way up as another" (lines 16-17)?** **(2)**
>
> She thinks the Lizard is so stupid that it will have nothing to add to the trial, even if it can see everything.

Any answer stating that the Lizard is unintelligent is likely to get two marks. There are two available because Alice's words might be confusing.

> **4.** **"Upset" in line 18 has two possible meanings. What are they?** **(2)**
>
> **(i)** Knocked over
>
> **(ii)** Made unhappy

> **5.** **Why in lines 29-30 does the White Rabbit speak "in a very respectful tone" while "frowning and making faces"?** **(3)**
>
> The White Rabbit wants to persuade the King that Alice's comment is "unimportant", so he treats him with respect to win his sympathy. At the same time, he pulls "faces" to make the King feel that his previous opinion was foolish and should be changed.

There is one mark for explaining why he behaves with "respect", and another for saying why he makes "faces". The third mark is for making clear what the White Rabbit's overall aim is.

It might be difficult to work this out from the question, but a couple of rules will keep you safe:

- Rule one is **explain everything quoted in a question** (so in this case each quote needs a separate comment).
- Rule two is **always give a direct answer to the question** (in this case, "Why?").

If you did both of these things, you will probably have got full marks.

> **6.**   **What do lines 31-33 suggest about the King's personality?** **(3)**
>
> He is too proud to admit that he is wrong ("Unimportant, of course, I meant"). He is also indecisive, trying out the two words ("important – unimportant") repeatedly.

There is a mark for each point, and an extra mark for development or well-chosen evidence. The answer above is quite secure because it provides evidence for each point.

Any sensible opinion which fits the evidence is acceptable here.

> **7.**   **Why does Alice think that "it doesn't matter a bit" that "some of the jury wrote down 'important' and some 'unimportant'" (line 35)?** **(2)**
>
> Because she knows "nothing", it is irrelevant to the trial whether her evidence is "important" or "unimportant".

Any clear explanation (which makes sense) is fine here.

> **8.**   **In the end, the jury will need to decide whether the Knave of Hearts is guilty. Basing your answer on evidence from the text, how much would you trust their decision?** **(6)**
>
> Their verdict would be as reliable as flipping a coin. They can't do much by themselves, for example when they are "sprawling" and Alice has to put them back. They are often very stupid, such as when the Lizard gazes at the roof "with its mouth open". Finally, they are very unlikely to agree: some write down "important" and some "unimportant".

It's very important that you clearly answer the "How much?" question, probably at the beginning or the end of your answer. Apart from that, you have a fair amount of flexibility in how you construct your response.

The example is very safe, because it answers the question and provides three pairs of point/evidence. However, two evidenced points, one of them with some extra explanation, would probably be adequate.

Having said this, it is always better not to take a risk if you can avoid it: underline plenty of evidence and plan a full answer.

---

9.   **(a) Write down, from four different sentences in the passage:**   **(2)**

       (i) an adjective

important

       (ii) a noun

shock

       (iii) a verb

jumped

       (iv) an adverb

quickly

Any correct answer is acceptable. There is half a mark available for each part of the question.

(b) Invent a single sentence that uses all four words in (a) correctly.   **(2)**

My mum woke with a shock, jumped up, and quickly strode off to her important meeting.

You get two marks for a sentence with your four words correctly used. There are no marks for creativity!

Be careful not to make a mistake elsewhere in your sentence and lose a mark that way.

10.   **What does Alice think about this trial and the people involved in it? Support your answer with evidence.**   **(6)**

Alice wishes to be courteous to the court, because she instinctively respects it: "I beg your pardon!" she says. On the other hand, she finds the individual figures unimpressive, for example when the Lizard seems "as much use" upside-down. In the end, she doesn't care: "it doesn't matter a bit".

The three most likely points (in my opinion) are in the example above.

It might be possible to get six marks with fewer than three points, if you explain very fully and the marker is on your side, but I would not feel confident doing this.

Just like with an "impressions of character" question, the way to solve this is to **find a number of places where a character says or does something, then work out what each one teaches you**. The opposite approach (working out what you think before finding evidence) is more difficult and tends to produce worse answers, because the quotes often end up not matching the arguments they are supposed to reinforce.

The challenging aspect of this question is that Alice has a reserved character, so it takes a bit of work to deduce what she is thinking.

END

Paper 4: *Breakfast With Fagin*

Type B: Intermediate Level

Oliver, an orphan, has just been introduced to the elderly Fagin by the Artful Dodger and Charley Bates.

"You'd like to be able to make pocket-handkerchiefs as easy as Charley Bates, wouldn't you, my dear?" said the old man.

"Very much, indeed, if you'll teach me, sir," replied Oliver.

Master Bates saw something so exquisitely ludicrous in this reply, that he burst into
5   another laugh; which laugh, meeting the coffee he was drinking, and carrying it down some wrong channel, very nearly terminated in his premature suffocation.

"He is so jolly green!" said Charley when he recovered, as an apology to the company for his unpolite behaviour.

The Dodger said nothing, but he smoothed Oliver's hair over his eyes, and said he'd
10   know better, by and by; upon which the old gentleman, observing Oliver's colour mounting, changed the subject by asking whether there had been much of a crowd at the execution that morning? This made him wonder more and more; for it was plain from the replies of the two boys that they had both been there; and Oliver naturally wondered how they could possibly have found time to be so very industrious.

15   When the breakfast was cleared away; the merry old gentleman and the two boys played at a very curious and uncommon game, which was performed in this way. The merry old gentleman, placing a snuff-box in one pocket of his trousers, a note-case in the other, and a watch in his waistcoat pocket, with a guard-chain round his neck, and sticking a mock diamond pin in his shirt: buttoned his coat tight round him, and
20   putting his spectacle-case and handkerchief in his pockets, trotted up and down the room with a stick, in imitation of the manner in which old gentlemen walk about the streets any hour in the day. Sometimes he stopped at the fire-place, and sometimes at the door, making believe that he was staring with all his might into shop-windows. At such times, he would look constantly round him, for fear of thieves, and would
25   keep slapping all his pockets in turn, to see that he hadn't lost anything, in such a very funny and natural manner, that Oliver laughed till the tears ran down his face. All this time, the two boys followed him closely about: getting out of his sight, so nimbly, every time he turned round, that it was impossible to follow their motions. At last, the Dodger trod upon his toes, or ran upon his boot accidently, while Charley Bates

30   stumbled up against him behind; and in that one moment they took from him, with
the most extraordinary rapidity, snuff-box, note-case, watch-guard, chain, shirt-pin,
pocket-handkerchief, even the spectacle-case. If the old gentleman felt a hand in any
one of his pockets, he cried out where it was; and then the game began all over again.

When this game had been played a great many times, a couple of young ladies called
35   to see the young gentleman; one of whom was named Bet, and the other Nancy. They
wore a good deal of hair, not very neatly turned up behind, and were rather untidy
about the shoes and stockings. They were not exactly pretty, perhaps; but they had a
great deal of colour in their faces, and looked quite stout and hearty. Being remarkably
free and agreeable in their manners, Oliver thought them very nice girls indeed. As
40   there is no doubt they were.

The visitors stopped a long time. Spirits were produced, in consequence of one of the
young ladies complaining of a coldness in her inside; and the conversation took a very
convivial and improving turn. At length, Charley Bates expressed his opinion that it
was time to pad the hoof. This, it occurred to Oliver, must be French for going out; for
45   directly afterwards, the Dodger, and Charley, and the two young ladies, went away
together, having been kindly furnished by the amiable old man with money to spend.

"There, my dear," said Fagin. "That's a pleasant life, isn't it? They have gone out for
the day."

"Have they done work, sir?" inquired Oliver.

Adapted from *Oliver Twist*, by Charles Dickens

1.   Where were the Dodger and Charley earlier in the morning?   **(1)**

2.   Explain the meaning of:

   (a) Green (line 7)   **(1)**

   (b) Industrious (line 14)   **(1)**

   (c) Stopped (line 41)   **(1)**

3.   Why does the Dodger "smooth Oliver's hair over his eyes" (line 9)?   **(3)**

4.   Carefully re-read lines 15-33.

   (a) What do the boys have to try and do in this game?   **(2)**

   (b) Why does Oliver laugh in line 26?   **(2)**

   (c) Why do the boys try to tread on Fagin's toes and "run upon his boot"?   **(2)**

   (d) What causes the boys to lose the game?   **(2)**

5.   Describe the appearance of the "young ladies" in your own words.   **(4)**

6.   "As there is no doubt they were" (lines 39-40) would usually be seen as an incomplete sentence. Why do you think the author has written it in this way?

   (3)

7.   Why does Oliver think that Charley is speaking in French (line 44)?   **(2)**

8.   **(a)** List two different adjectives (apart from "old") used in the text to describe Fagin.   **(2)**

   (b) What do these adjectives suggest about him?   **(2)**

   (c) Do you think that your answer to **(b)** is likely to be an accurate view of Fagin's character? Explain your answer.   **(2)**

9.   Why does Charley laugh (lines 4-5)?   **(4)**

10.   Imagine that the boys really do "make pocket-handkerchiefs" (as Fagin says in line 1). Continue the story from line 14 (ignore lines 15-49 of the passage), describing the scene. Make good use of the senses, and try to write about ten lines.   **(6)**

11.   The boys do not make handkerchiefs. What, bearing in mind your understanding of the passage, do they *really* do for a living?   **(2)**

TOTAL MARKS: 42

Blank Page

Breakfast With Fagin – Solutions

*Like the Alice in Wonderland comprehension, this contains a large number of questions, mostly worth a small number of marks each. The particular challenge of this exercise is that a number of them require a strong overall understanding of the passage. If you have not read the text thoroughly, you risk being caught out. This is why the general advice sheet (included in this pack) recommends reading each passage before **and after** reading the questions, before you start work.*

1.	**Where were the Dodger and Charley earlier in the morning?**	**(1)**

They were at a hanging ("the execution").

You might be tempted to say that they were at home earlier in the morning – but this would be a guess. There is no evidence *in the text* to support it.

2.	**Explain the meaning of:**	
	(a) Green (line 7)	**(1)**

This means "inexperienced" [**or** "innocent" **or** "naïve" etc.].

(b) Industrious (line 14)   **(1)**

This means "hard-working".

(c) Stopped (line 41)   **(1)**

This means "stayed".

Be careful to explain the meanings of these words **as they are used in the passage**. For example, "green" and "stopped" usually have different meanings from these. Also, be careful not to change the tenses or parts of speech of the words. For example, "stopped" is a verb in the past tense, so you must not write "stay" or "remain": either of these would be likely to lose half a mark.

"Green" and "industrious" are difficult, but the context should give you a good chance of coming close. **Always read the sentences before and after the one including a word very carefully** when you need to work out what it means.

> ### 3.　Why does the Dodger "smooth Oliver's hair over his eyes" (line 9)?　(3)
>
> He does this to show that he is superior to Oliver: he can touch him without asking. Also, he is moving Oliver's hair to make him look as young as possible, to emphasise how inexperienced ("green") he is – and how grown-up he himself is, by comparison.

Because this is worth three marks, you probably need to make more than one point. It's a difficult question, because the answer is not given directly in the passage.

You have to imagine that you are the Dodger and that you do this to Oliver: What are your reasons for it?

> ### 4.　Carefully re-read lines 15-33.
>
> #### (a) What do the boys have to try and do in this game?　(2)
>
> They have to keep "out of sight" until they have a chance to take everything from Fagin's pockets.
>
> #### (b) Why does Oliver laugh in line 26?　(2)
>
> He does this because the old man's acting is so "funny" and "natural" – he looks just like a worried "old gentleman", walking down the street.
>
> #### (c) Why do the boys try to tread on Fagin's toes and "run upon his boot"?　(2)
>
> They do this to distract him, so that he will not notice them take things from his pockets.
>
> #### (d) What causes the boys to lose the game?　(2)
>
> If Fagin feels a hand in his pocket he calls out where it is, in which case the boys lose and must begin again.

These answers just need to be short, clear and correct. The questions' purpose is to test understanding, so that is what you have to show.

Very short quotations are a good way to demonstrate that you know what is going on, but **avoid longer quotes**: they can create the impression that you don't properly understand the text, so are copying it instead.

- Be very careful not to confuse "what" and "why". For example, don't answer **(a)** by saying that the boys are practising to be thieves.

> **5.   Describe the appearance of the "young ladies" in your own words.   (4)**
>
> The women have lots of messy hair, clipped up to the backs of their heads. Their footwear and socks are also messy. Although they are not beautiful, their skin looks full of life. They are chubby and seem to have plenty of energy.

Notice that "free and agreeable" does not refer to their appearance.

You need to deal with at least **four out of the following five things**, making each point clearly **in your own words**, so that your understanding is obvious: hair; shoes & socks; lack of beauty; stoutness; "hearty" appearance.

> **6.   "As there is no doubt they were" (lines 39-40) would usually be seen as an incomplete sentence. Why do you think the author has written it in this way?   (3)**
>
> This might suggest that the narrator is a little hesitant: he is less confident than he claims to be that the women are "very nice". On the other hand, he might in fact be worried about accidentally suggesting that they are not nice: it is as though he is adding on this point, to make clear that there is "no doubt" about it.

The answer above is very safe, because it discusses two alternative possibilities. This is often an option available to you, and it can get you out of a corner when you cannot find a way to make one argument worth enough marks – so long as you make it clear that the arguments contradict ("on the other hand" or "alternatively" can do this).

However, I would probably give either sentence in the example three marks, because each of them shows understanding and develops an explanation sufficiently to be worth a good score.

The most important thing is to deal directly with *why* the sentence has been written this way: you need to think about **the narrator's thoughts**, and/or the sentence's **effect on the reader**.

> **7.   Why does Oliver think that Charley is speaking in French (line 44)?   (2)**
>
> Charley is speaking slang ("pad the hoof") which Oliver does not understand. He probably thinks it is French because Charley seems so knowledgeable to him.

The first sentence in the example might not be quite enough by itself, because it does not explain why Oliver thinks that it is *French* (as opposed to English slang).

A French-speaking pupil tells me that (perhaps by coincidence) a similar phrase does exist in French.

---

8.   (a) List two different adjectives (apart from "old") used in the text to describe Fagin. **(2)**

merry; amiable

This is surprisingly tricky, because Dickens uses adjectives sparingly.

(b) What do these adjectives suggest about him? **(2)**

They suggest that he is friendly and kind: an easy person to get along with.

This is a fairly simple question so long as you do what it asks: you need to explain <u>what the adjectives from **(a)** suggest</u>, not what you *actually* think Fagin is like.

Even if you did not find two adjectives for **(a)**, you should still try to write something here, based on the passage's descriptions of Fagin: it might be worth a mark.

(c) Do you think that your answer to (b) is likely to be an accurate view of Fagin's character? Explain your answer. **(2)**

I do not, because although he seems friendly, in fact he is teaching the children to steal. Furthermore, he is a very good actor (for example when he makes Oliver laugh), so I would not trust the way he seems to be.

You could make the opposite case, though it might be difficult to explain convincingly.

Although short, this question requires you to have a good overview of Fagin's behaviour in the text. Either one of the two points in the example might well be enough – but if you can think of two things to say (and, in an exam, if you have time), say them.

If **(b)** is wrong, but your answer to **(c)** is a sensible response to what you *did* write, it should still get the marks.

---

9.   Why does Charley laugh (lines 4-5)?   **(4)**

Charley laughs because he finds it ridiculous ("exquisitely ludicrous") that Oliver believes Fagin's story about the boys making handkerchiefs. He probably also finds it funny that Oliver treats Fagin so politely ("if you'll teach me, sir") – as though Fagin is a real gentleman, rather than a seedy old thief.

This is challenging: firstly, because you need to have a good overall understanding of the passage to know why the idea of Charley making handkerchiefs is silly; and secondly, because you need more than one point to have a chance of four marks.

Just because the question includes a reference to "lines 4-5" (where Charley Bates laughs), this does not mean that the reason "why" he does this will not be elsewhere.

You should begin an answer like this by re-reading several lines before and after lines 4-5, and underlining any useful clues. Both of the quotes used in the example were uncovered like this.

---

10.   Imagine that the boys really do "make pocket-handkerchiefs" (as Fagin says in line 1). Continue the story from line 14 (ignore lines 15-49 of the passage), describing the scene. Make good use of the senses, and try to write about ten lines.   **(6)**

However, the answer was quickly apparent. The boys hauled endless reams of silk thread from every hidden pocket, so that the carpet was quickly awash with reels and spools of all conceivable colours.

For a while there was no sound except the "phut" and "swish" of needles breaking cloth. Occasionally the old gentleman looked up approvingly, but Oliver saw how his eyebrows darkened viciously whenever he noticed a strand out of place.

As for himself, Oliver stood very still, unnoticed, his rough fingers pressed nervously into his palms. Despite the fusty-smelling dust which clustered ticklishly in his throat, he dared not sneeze, or in any way ruffle the thread of silence which stretched itself tight across the room.

Show that you are **continuing the ideas from the passage** (up to line 14). Oliver has just been wondering "how" the boys find time to be "so very industrious", so the example uses this as a link, referring to "the answer" to Oliver's question.

The question invites you to use "the senses", so make an effort to use as many of them as possible. The example uses sight, hearing, touch and smell. It also uses metaphor ("the thread of silence") and onomatopoeia ("phut … swish"). All this might seem over-written (too fancy) outside an exercise like this, but that doesn't matter here.

Make sure that your answer relates to the manufacture of pocket handkerchiefs in some way.

Keep characterization from the passage as far as you can. In the example, although Charley and the Dodger become subdued, Fagin and Oliver are presented with strong character traits.

In any creative question, you risk losing marks if you make mistakes with your English.

> **11. The boys do not make handkerchiefs. What, bearing in mind your understanding of the passage, do they *really* do for a living?** (2)
>
> They really pick people's pockets for valuable items, which they bring to Fagin (who probably sells them).

Because this is only worth two marks, you don't need to give evidence.

The question is testing your understanding of the text: if you haven't worked the answer out, you probably did not read the passage with enough thought before beginning to write your answers.

END

Blank Page

Paper 5: *War In The Desert*

Type C: Challenging Level

T. E. Lawrence, who is writing here about one of his experiences during the First World War, is commonly known as "Lawrence of Arabia".

At last, near noon, in a snatch of fine weather, the watchmen on the south peak flagged their cloaks wildly in signal of a train. We reached our positions in an instant, for we had squatted the late hours on our heels in a streaming ditch near the line, so as not to miss another chance. The Arabs took cover properly. I looked back at their ambush
5   from my firing point, and saw nothing but the grey hillsides.

I could not hear the train coming, but trusted, and knelt ready for perhaps half an hour, when the suspense became intolerable, and I signalled to know what was up. They sent down to say it was coming very slowly, and was an enormously long train. Our appetites stiffened. The longer it was the more would be the loot. Then came word
10   that it had stopped. It moved again.

Finally, near one o'clock, I heard it panting. The locomotive was evidently defective (all these wood-fired trains were bad), and the heavy load on the up-gradient was proving too much for its capacity. I crouched behind my bush, while it crawled slowly into view past the south cutting, and along the bank above my head towards the
15   culvert. The first ten trucks were open trucks, crowded with troops. However, once again it was too late to choose, so when the engine was squarely over the mine I pushed down the handle of the exploder. Nothing happened. I sawed it up and down four times.

Still nothing happened; and I realized that it had gone out of order, and that I was
20   kneeling on a naked bank, with a Turkish troop train crawling past fifty yards away. The bush, which had seemed a foot high, shrank smaller than a fig-leaf; and I felt myself the most distinct object in the country-side. Behind me was an open valley for two hundred yards to the cover where my Arabs were waiting and wondering what I was at. It was impossible to make a bolt for it, or the Turks would step off the train
25   and finish us. If I sat still, there might be just a hope of my being ignored as a casual Bedouin.

So there I sat, counting for sheer life, while eighteen open trucks, three box-waggons, and three officers' coaches dragged by. The engine panted slower and slower, and I thought every moment that it would break down. The troops took no great notice of
30   me, but the officers were interested, and came out to the little platforms at the ends of

their carriages, pointing and staring. I waved back at them, grinning nervously, and feeling an improbable shepherd in my Meccan dress, with its twisted golden circlet about my head. Perhaps the mud-stains, the wet and their ignorance made me accepted. The end of the brake van slowly disappeared into the cutting on the north.

35 As it went, I jumped up, buried my wires, snatched hold of the wretched exploder, and went like a rabbit uphill into safety. There I took breath and looked back to see that the train had finally stuck. It waited, about five hundred yards beyond the mine, for nearly an hour to get up a head of steam, while an officers' patrol came back and searched, very carefully, the ground where I had been seen sitting. However, the wires

40 were properly hidden: they found nothing: the engine plucked up heart again, and away they went.

From *Seven Pillars of Wisdom* by T. E. Lawrence

1.   How long does the train take, from when it is spotted to its arrival?   **(2)**

....

2.   Two different words suggest that the train is like a living thing.

        (a) What are they?   **(2)**

....

        (b) Why might the author have used these words?   **(4)**

....

....

....

....

....

3.   Why does Lawrence say (line 5) that he "saw nothing but the grey hillsides"?
                                                                                                                        (2)

....

....

....

....

4.   Why are Lawrence and his companions excited that the train is "enormously
        long" (line 8)?   **(2)**

....

....

5.   Explain why the bush "shrank smaller than a fig leaf" (line 21)?   **(5)**

....

....

....

....

....

....

6.   What do you think "Bedouin" means (line 26)?   **(2)**

....

7.   Why is Lawrence "counting for sheer life" (line 27)?   **(3)**

....

....

....

....

....

8.   Write down a simile from the text.   **(2)**

....

9.   Explain, giving evidence from the text to support your points, what Lawrence and the Arabs have been planning to do.   **(8)**

....

....

....

....

....

....

....

10.   The book's next sentence is below, without punctuation or capital letters. Re-write it correctly. Do not divide it into more than one sentence.   **(10)**

mifleh was past tears thinking I had intentionally let the train through and when the serahin had been told the real cause they said bad luck is with us

....

....

....

....

....

11.   The following extract contains four spelling mistakes.

Round the bend, whisteling its loudest, came the train, a splendid two-engined thing of twelve passenger coaches, travelling at top speed on the favouring grade. I touched of under the first driving wheel of the first locomotive, and the exploshun was terrific. The ground spouted blackly into my face, and I was sent spining, to sit up with the shirt torn to my shoulder and the blood dripping from long, ragged scratches on my left arm. Between my knees lay the exploder, crushed under a twisted sheet of sooty iron.

       (a) Circle the mistakes.   **(4)**

(b) Write the correct spellings here.   **(4)**

....

....

....

....

TOTAL MARKS: 50

Blank Page

War In The Desert – Solutions

This test is designed to challenge you with an unfamiliar structure. There are a lot of questions, and sometimes the number of marks does not match the number of things you need to say. There are also some spelling and grammar exercises, of a sort you have not faced so far in this pack. The passage contains some difficult language.

---

1.   **How long does the train take, from when it is spotted to its arrival?**   **(2)**
It takes about one hour.

The train is spotted "near noon" and reaches Lawrence "near one o'clock". "Perhaps half an hour" (line 6) is a trap for anybody who isn't reading carefully enough.

---

2.   **Two different words suggest that the train is like a living thing.**
(a) What are they?   **(2)**
They are "panting" and "crawling".
(b) Why might the author have used these words?   **(4)**
They show the effort with which the train moves, emphasising how slow and awkward "wood-fired" trains are: they "crawl" like elderly snakes. It might also create some sympathy for the train (not to mention its occupants), because we are encouraged to think of it as a living thing, "panting" (puffing steam) as it travels along the tracks, towards people who are waiting to kill it (blow it up).

You need to focus on the words' effect on the reader.

As you probably know, this is an example of **personification**. How do we think of the train differently when we consider it like a living thing or a person? You need two points, each well explained, for four marks.

> **3.   Why does Lawrence say (line 5) that he "saw nothing but the grey hillsides"?**   **(2)**
>
> His companions ("the Arabs") have hidden themselves in order to ambush the train. He is pleased that they are now completely concealed.

If you get the main point (that the Arabs have hidden themselves completely), you will probably get the marks.

Of course, as you have seen many times in this pack, it is best to be safe and say a little more.

> **4.   Why are Lawrence and his companions excited that the train is "enormously long" (line 8)?**   **(2)**
>
> This means that there will be lots of "loot" (useful or valuable items) to take from it.

The word "loot" is key. It is wise to define it if you can ("useful or valuable items"), but if you imply some understanding (e.g. the phrase "to take from it" in the example), you can reasonably expect to get both marks.

> **5.   Explain why the bush "shrank smaller than a fig leaf" (line 21)?**   **(5)**
>
> It had seemed big enough to hide behind, but now that the train is looking down on him it seems completely inadequate and he is worried that they will spot that he is not an Arab and has terrorist equipment. To be so exposed is also embarrassing, as though he is naked except for a "fig leaf".

This is a five mark question because it is difficult – not because you need to say five things. Some schools' exams include questions like this.

You would get five marks just for the first sentence of the example, which shows strong understanding.

The second sentence follows the principle that you should always discuss every part of a quotation given in a question – but in this case it might not be necessary.

"Fig leaf" also emphasises the bareness of the "naked bank", because Adam and Eve are traditionally said to have used fig leaves to cover their nakedness.

Another likely point is that Lawrence is worried about letting his comrades down.

---

6.   What do you think "Bedouin" means (line 26)?   (2)

A Bedouin is somebody who lives in the Arabian or Syrian deserts, traditionally travelling from place to place.

Anything close to this (that it is somebody who lives there, a native inhabitant, etc.) is fine. The question is testing your courage in the face of an unfamiliar word – not your cultural knowledge of the Middle East.

---

7.   Why is Lawrence "counting for sheer life" (line 27)?   (3)

He is "counting" the many "coaches" as they pass, willing the train on, hoping that it does not stop next to him (in which case the "Turks" might see that he is English or find his "exploder").

Any clear explanation that makes sense is acceptable. The meaning is not entirely clear from the passage, so you have to make an intelligent guess, based on what is happening in the text.

---

8.   Write down a simile from the text.   (2)

"went like a rabbit"

"Write down" means that you do not need a full sentence.

Don't let the two marks trick you into writing an unnecessary explanation. They are because this lonely simile is hard to find.

---

9.   Explain, giving evidence from the text to support your points, what Lawrence and the Arabs have been planning to do.   (8)

Their plan is to blow up the train as it travels past (Lawrence has an "exploder"), after which the Arabs will emerge from their "ambush" and attack the "coaches". When they have driven off or killed all the "Turks", they will "loot" the train, taking everything valuable or useful.

If you give a proper explanation of **the bombing, the attack** and **the looting**, preferably with quotes, you will get eight marks. You will start to lose marks if you miss anything, do not prove a point with evidence, or do not clearly explain your ideas.

This is the sort of question for which you would be particularly unwise to rely on your memory. Go back through the passage and **underline every relevant detail** before writing.

---

10. **The book's next sentence is below, without punctuation or capital letters. Re-write it correctly. Do not divide it into more than one sentence.** **(10)**

mifleh was past tears thinking I had intentionally let the train through and when the serahin had been told the real cause they said bad luck is with us

> Mifleh was past tears, thinking I had intentionally let the train through, and when the Serahin had been told the real cause, they said, "Bad luck is with us."

Take away one mark for every missing punctuation mark. The exception is the pair of commas before and after "they said": if you have either one of these, that is acceptable.

Also take away a mark for any extra mistake that is added to the sentence.

Many people believe that you cannot have a comma before "and". They are wrong. In this case, the comma is essential: "thinking I had intentionally let the train through" is a **subordinate clause** (extra information in the sentence) and *must* be separated using commas.

---

11. **The following extract contains four spelling mistakes.**

Round the bend, whisteling its loudest, came the train, a splendid two-engined thing of twelve passenger coaches, travelling at top speed on the favouring grade. I touched of under the first driving wheel of the first locomotive, and the exploshun was terrific. The ground spouted blackly into my face, and I was sent spining to sit up with the shirt torn to my shoulder and the blood dripping from long, ragged scratches on my left arm. Between my knees lay the exploder, crushed under a twisted sheet of sooty iron.

(a) Circle the mistakes. **(4)**

Be careful: each *extra* word circled loses a mark (though the minimum score is 0). It would be wise to circle in pencil, only using a pen when you are certain (and rubbing out any incorrect pencil marks).

Be aware that "travelling" is correct. "Traveling" is only usual in American English.

(b) Write the correct spellings here. **(4)**

whistling
off
explosion
spinning

There is one mark for each of the words above, written correctly.

END

Paper 6: *A Tempest & Two Leopards*

Type C: Challenging Level

Mary Kingsley was a famous explorer at the end of the Victorian period.

I once came upon a leopard.

I had got caught in a tornado in a dense forest. The massive, mighty trees were waving like a wheat-field in an autumn gale in England, and I dare say a field mouse in a wheat-field in a gale would have heard much the same uproar. The tornado shrieked
5   like ten thousand vengeful demons. The great trees creaked and groaned and strained against it and their bush-rope cables groaned and smacked like whips, and ever and anon a thundering crash with snaps like pistol shots told that they and their mighty tree had strained and struggled in vain. The fierce rain came in a roar, tearing to shreds the leaves and blossoms and deluging everything. I was making bad weather of it,
10   and climbing up over a lot of rocks out of a gully bottom where I had been half drowned in a stream, and on getting my head to the level of a block of rock I observed right in front of my eyes, broadside on, maybe a yard off, certainly not more, a big leopard.

He was crouching on the ground, with his magnificent head thrown back and his eyes
15   shut. His fore-paws were spread out in front of him and he lashed the ground with his tail, and I am sorry to say, in face of that awful danger — I don't mean me, but the tornado — that creature swore, softly, but repeatedly and profoundly. I did not notice all these facts in one glance, for no sooner did I see him than I ducked under the rocks, and remembered thankfully that leopards are said to have no power of smell. But I
20   heard his observation on the weather, and the flip-flap of his tail on the ground. Every now and then I cautiously took a look at him with one eye round a rock-edge, and he remained in the same position.

My feelings tell me he remained there twelve months, but my calmer judgment puts the time down at twenty minutes; and at last, on taking another cautious peep, I saw
25   he was gone. At the time I wished I knew exactly where, but I do not care about that detail now, for I saw no more of him. He had moved off in one of those weird lulls which you get in a tornado, when for a few seconds the wild herd of hurrying winds seem to have lost themselves, and wander round crying and wailing like lost souls, until their common rage seizes them again and they rush back to their work of
30   destruction.

It was an immense pleasure to have seen the great creature like that. He was so evidently enraged and baffled by the uproar and dazzled by the floods of lightning that swept down into the deepest recesses of the forest, showing at one second every detail of twig, leaf, branch, and stone round you, and then leaving you in a sort of
35 swirling dark until the next flash came; this, and the great conglomerate roar of the wind, rain and thunder, was enough to bewilder any living thing.

***

I have never hurt a leopard intentionally; I am habitually kind to animals, and besides I do not think it is ladylike to go shooting things with a gun. Twice, however, I have been in collision with them. On one occasion a big leopard had attacked a dog, who,
40 with her family, was occupying a broken-down hut next to mine. The dog was a half-bred boarhound, and a savage brute on her own account. I, being roused by the uproar, rushed out into the feeble moonlight, thinking she was having one of her habitual turns-up with other dogs, and I saw a whirling mass of animal matter within a yard of me. I fired two mushroom-shaped native chairs in rapid succession into the
45 brown of it, and the meeting broke up into a leopard and a dog. The leopard crouched, I think to spring on me. I can see its great, beautiful, lambent eyes still, and I seized an earthen water-cooler and flung it straight at them. It was a noble shot; it burst on the leopard's head like a shell and the leopard went for bush.

Twenty minutes later people began to drop in cautiously and inquire if anything was
50 the matter, and I civilly asked them to go and ask the leopard in the bush, but they firmly refused. We found the dog had got her shoulder slit open as if by a blow from a cutlass, and the leopard had evidently seized the dog by the scruff of her neck, but owing to the loose folds of skin no bones were broken and she got round all right after much ointment from me, which she paid me for with several bites.

Adapted from *Travels in West Africa*, by Mary Kingsley

1.   Write down one word with the same meaning as each of the following, as used in the passage:

   (a) broadside (line 12)   **(2)**

   (b) conglomerate (line 35)   **(2)**

   (c) bewilder (line 36)   **(2)**

   (d) civilly (line 50)   **(2)**

2.   Explain the comparison between the narrator (Mary Kingsley) and a "field mouse" (lines 3-4).   **(3)**

3.   Why is Kingsley "thankful" that "leopards are said to have no power of smell" (line 19)?   **(2)**

4.   What is meant by the phrase, "I heard his observation on the weather" (line 19-20)?   **(3)**

5.   In your own words, describe the behaviour of the leopard in lines 14-22.   **(5)**

6.   **(a)** Write down three similes from the passage.   **(3)**

   (b) Which simile do you find most effective? Explain your choice.   **(4)**

7.   Write down an example of alliteration from the passage.   **(2)**

8.   Each of the following sentences contains two mistakes. Re-write each sentence correctly.   **(6)**

   (i) I saw alot of leopards in those days, so I became used to there habits.

   (ii) The dog licked it's fur firmley.

   (iii) The hunter, a glint in his eye asked me, "So, what are you doing out here, Miss."

9. Why does Kingsley tell people to "go and ask the leopard in the bush" (line 50)? **(2)**

10. Explain fully why the dog doesn't break any bones when savaged by the leopard. **(3)**

11. How does the dog respond when treated with ointment by Kingsley? **(1)**

12. How similar is Mary Kingsley to other explorers you have heard of? Explain your answer fully, giving evidence from the passage. **(8)**

TOTAL MARKS: 50

Blank Page

A Tempest & Two Leopards – **Solutions**

This exercise presents similar challenges to the previous one, though without the assistance of guide lines to help you decide how much to write. As you will have discovered, however, its subject matter is quite different. Its distinctive characteristics are that it is very descriptive, and that it is divided into two separate narratives about two different leopards.

---

1. **Write down one word with the same meaning as each of the following, as used in the passage:**

(a) broadside (line 12) (2)

sideways

(b) conglomerate (line 35) (2)

combined

(c) bewilder (line 36) (2)

confuse

(d) civilly (line 50) (2)

politely

An incorrect answer that would still make good sense in the text could receive one mark.

Pay attention to the question: it asks for "one word", and if you use more than that in an answer, you will lose a mark. Similarly, you will lose a mark if you use the wrong part of speech (e.g. a verb instead of a noun). Here is an answer to **(d)** that would get no marks, because it loses a mark twice:

She is being polite.

"Polite" is an adjective, rather than an adverb like "civilly"; also, the answer uses more than one word. Perhaps this is harsh – but for this reason you must read every question very carefully.

> **2.   Explain the comparison between the narrator (Mary Kingsley) and a "field mouse" (lines 3-4).   (3)**
>
> She is the same size in relation to the trees of the forest as a mouse is in relation to a field of wheat. Kingsley thinks that, to a field mouse, an English storm would sound as loud as this "tornado" does to her.

It is fairly straightforward to work out what Kingsley is trying to say; it is more difficult to express it clearly and simply. You have to explain the comparison of noises clearly, and it will be difficult to do this without explaining how the relative sizes of a human and a mouse relate to the different surroundings of a field of crops and a jungle.

> **3.   Why is Kingsley "thankful" that "leopards are said to have no power of smell" (line 19)?   (2)**
>
> She has hidden "under the rocks", and the leopard has not yet spotted her. If it could smell, it might find her and attack her.

There are two elements to this: that the leopard might find her if it could smell, and that it would be dangerous if it did.

Kingsley is wrong: leopards have a fairly good sense of smell. She was just lucky.

> **4.   What is meant by the phrase, "I heard his observation on the weather" (lines 19-20)?   (3)**
>
> She is referring to the leopard's grumbling sound, which seems so angry, almost human, that she says "that creature swore". It is as though he is complaining about the weather.

You need to explain that the quote refers to his growling, and that the author is comparing this to a person talking about bad weather. If you have both these things, you are likely to get three marks.

The lesson of this question is to read the context of a quote (below and above) carefully, because the most useful information is sometimes a few lines away.

> **5.** **In your own words, describe the behaviour of the leopard in lines 14-22.**
> **(5)**
>
> The leopard stays where he is, close to the floor, his head looking up but his eyes closed. With his front limbs apart for balance, he beats the ground violently with his tail, growling angrily in a low voice.

The crucial points are that the leopard **beats the ground** and **growls**, but **does not move** from his position. These points, made clearly in your own words, might be sufficient, but another two or three points would be wise so that you get five ticks and therefore a clear five marks.

Note that it is **essential to say that the leopard stays in the same place**, because this is in line 22: if the question did not want this, it would only have asked you to consider lines 14-17.

For this sort of question, as you probably know by now, first underline all the relevant information in the section. Work out how you would clearly explain each thing to an imaginary person sat in the room with you, without repeating any important words from the text.

> **6.** **(a) Write down three similes from the passage.** **(3)**
>
> "The tornado shrieked like ten thousand vengeful demons."
> "snaps like pistol shots"
> "it burst … like a shell"

As you know, "write down" means "list". Any three similes will do.

It is a good idea to include both halves of the comparison (e.g. both "snaps" and "pistol shots"). Notice how, in the third example, "…" is used to show that some words have been missed out.

> **(b) Which simile do you find most effective? Explain your choice.** **(4)**
>
> I find the first one most effective, because it suggests how the violence of the storm is almost supernatural: it is like a curse, bringing "demons". "Shrieked" powerfully represents the wailing of the wind as being like a cry of pain or anger.

For four marks, you need to properly develop two points: this is easiest if you explain two different parts of the simile. Here, the answer is based on the words "demons" and "shrieked".

A completely logical answer would explain why one simile is "most" effective by also discussing why the others are *less* powerful. However, there are only four marks available, so it is enough to focus on your chosen quotation. This is what the marker will be expecting.

You may also have noticed by this point that the tests in this book ask questions about **similes** more than **metaphors**. This is because metaphors are less commonly tested at 11-plus – although you may have studied them at school, and should be prepared to write about them. This shouldn't stop you using them impressively in your creative writing.

7.	Write down an example of alliteration from the passage.	(2)

"a half-bred boarhound, and a savage brute"

This example alliterates with "b … b … b". There are two marks because finding an example requires some skill.

You don't need to explain your choice: the question only asks you to "write down" a quotation.

These papers deal with **alliteration** but not **assonance**: I have never seen knowledge of assonance tested at 11-plus.

8.	Each of the following sentences contains two mistakes. Re-write each sentence correctly.	(6)

(i) I saw alot of leopards in those days, so I became used to there habits.

I saw a lot of leopards in those days, so I became used to their habits.

(ii) The dog licked it's fur firmley.

The dog licked its fur firmly.

"It's" is always short for "it is". It is a **contraction** of "it is", because an "I" has been left out.

Don't put an apostrophe in "its" when it means "belonging to it": this is like "my", "your", "her", "his", and so on. The technical way of saying this is: **Possessive pronouns do not take apostrophes** (except in the case of "one's").

> **(iii) The hunter, a glint in his eye asked me, "So, what are you doing out here, Miss."**
>
> The hunter, a glint in his eye, asked me, "So, what are you doing out here, Miss?"

"A glint in his eye" is extra information (a subordinate clause). The rest of the sentence would work fine without it ("The hunter asked me ..."), so the added information needs to be put in commas.

Another way of thinking about it is that you would pause where the commas are.

"Miss" can be written with or without a capital letter.

As for the question mark ... it is amazing how many people forget these.

> **9.   Why does Kingsley tell people to "go and ask the leopard in the bush" (line 50)?**   **(2)**
>
> She is amazed that they have only come out once the danger has passed and she no longer needs help. If they feel like asking stupid questions, they should try fighting a leopard themselves.

The most important thing is to understand that she is not actually telling people to go and ask the leopard something: she is being sarcastic. If you have understood that, you may only need to make one point. However, I wouldn't risk it. A belt-and-braces answer like the example is always safest.

> **10.   Explain fully why the dog doesn't break any bones when savaged by the leopard.**   **(3)**
>
> When the leopard grabs the dog by "the scruff", its teeth only break through "loose skin" and come out on the other side. Because the skin has stretched away from the dog's body, the leopard does not hit bone.

You are free to use quotes or not, because the emphasis is on explaining. You have to show that you clearly understand the key ideas, which are set out in the example above.

If you do quote (which is often a good idea), be careful that you do not just repeat the passage: you need to demonstrate understanding.

> **11.   How does the dog respond when treated with ointment by Kingsley?   (1)**
>
> It bites her "several" times.

It should be enough to say that it bites her.

> **12.   How similar is Mary Kingsley to other explorers you have heard of? Explain your answer fully, giving evidence from the passage.   (8)**
>
> Like many explorers, she is willing to confront danger (such as being "half drowned"), even travelling alone through the jungle. She has a fascination with nature, and finds it an "immense pleasure" to have seen such a rare sight: the search for unusual things is often an important motivation for explorers.
>
> On the other hand, she is not boastful like some explorers I have heard of, who want to be the heroes of their stories: she admits weaknesses (such as when "I was making bad weather of it"). Moreover, she is not interested in hunting animals and taking trophies (a popular activity at the time), saying that it is not "ladylike". In fact, I have not heard of another Victorian woman who was an explorer.
>
> Although she has some similarities with other explorers, overall Kingsley strikes me as a very unusual figure, with her own way of seeing things.

This is quite a tricky question. You have to **re-read the passage very carefully, hunting for clues and underlining them**.

A "how similar" question like this can be approached in several different ways: in this case you could argue that she is totally different from other explorers, or exactly the same – so long as you can find enough points to make one case or the other. However, it is much easier (and more convincing) to say that there are similarities and differences, as the example does.

You should be careful to **include a definite answer to the question** ("How similar?"), as the final paragraph here does. You might get away with leaving this out, but don't take the risk: a tough examiner might remove a mark or two if you don't say what your overall opinion is.

The eight marks are likely to be for four points, each with some evidence from the passage. Because there is hardly any information about other explorers in the text, **you are not expected to give examples to show what *is* usual**: you just need to show what Kingsley does and says and comment on it sensibly. However, you do need to say how each thing makes her similar or different from *how you imagine* other explorers to be.

If you **have** made specific comparisons with explorers you know about, these should get credit, and in this way it might be possible to get eight marks with three or (if your explanations are very detailed) two main points.

END

Paper 7: *Rikki-tikki-tavi*

Type D: Advanced Level

This story (from The Jungle Book*) is set in India.*

This is the story of the great war that Rikki-tikki-tavi fought single-handed, through the bath-rooms of the big bungalow in Segowlee cantonment. Darzee, the tailorbird, helped him, and Chuchundra, the musk-rat, who never comes out into the middle of the floor, but always creeps round by the wall, gave him advice, but Rikki-tikki did
5 the real fighting.

He was a mongoose, rather like a little cat in his fur and his tail, but quite like a weasel in his head and his habits. His eyes and the end of his restless nose were pink. He could scratch himself anywhere he pleased with any leg, front or back, that he chose to use. He could fluff up his tail till it looked like a bottle brush, and his war cry as he
10 scuttled through the long grass was: "Rikk-tikk-tikki-tikki-tchk!"

One day, a high summer flood washed him out of the burrow where he lived with his father and mother, and carried him, kicking and clucking, down a roadside ditch. He found a little wisp of grass floating there, and clung to it till he lost his senses. When he revived, he was lying in the hot sun on the middle of a garden path, very draggled
15 indeed, and a small boy was saying, "Here's a dead mongoose. Let's have a funeral."

"No," said his mother, "let's take him in and dry him. Perhaps he isn't really dead."

They took him into the house, and a big man picked him up between his finger and thumb and said he was not dead but half choked. So they wrapped him in cotton wool, and warmed him over a little fire, and he opened his eyes and sneezed.

20 "Now," said the big man (he was an Englishman who had just moved into the bungalow), "don't frighten him, and we'll see what he'll do."

It is the hardest thing in the world to frighten a mongoose, because he is eaten up from nose to tail with curiosity. The motto of all the mongoose family is "Run and find out," and Rikki-tikki was a true mongoose. He looked at the cotton wool, decided that it
25 was not good to eat, ran all round the table, sat up and put his fur in order, scratched himself, and jumped on the small boy's shoulder.

"Don't be frightened, Teddy," said his father. "That's his way of making friends."

"Ouch! He's tickling under my chin," said Teddy.

Rikki-tikki looked down between the boy's collar and neck, snuffed at his ear, and
30   climbed down to the floor, where he sat rubbing his nose.

"Good gracious," said Teddy's mother, "and that's a wild creature! I suppose he's so
tame because we've been kind to him."

"All mongooses are like that," said her husband. "If Teddy doesn't pick him up by the
tail, or try to put him in a cage, he'll run in and out of the house all day long. Let's give
35   him something to eat."

They gave him a little piece of raw meat. Rikki-tikki liked it immensely, and when it
was finished he went out into the veranda and sat in the sunshine and fluffed up his
fur to make it dry to the roots. Then he felt better.

"There are more things to find out about in this house," he said to himself, "than all
40   my family could find out in all their lives. I shall certainly stay and find out."

He spent all that day roaming over the house. He nearly drowned himself in the bath-
tubs, put his nose into the ink on a writing table, and burned it on the end of the big
man's cigar, for he climbed up in the big man's lap to see how writing was done. At
nightfall he ran into Teddy's nursery to watch how kerosene lamps were lighted, and
45   when Teddy went to bed Rikki-tikki climbed up too. But he was a restless companion,
because he had to get up and attend to every noise all through the night, and find out
what made it. Teddy's mother and father came in, the last thing, to look at their boy,
and Rikki-tikki was awake on the pillow. "I don't like that," said Teddy's mother. "He
may bite the child."

50   "He'll do no such thing," said the father. "Teddy's safer with that little beast than if he
had a bloodhound to watch him. If a snake came into the nursery now—"

But Teddy's mother wouldn't think of anything so awful.

From *The Jungle Book*, by Rudyard Kipling

1. List three things about Rikki-tikki's behaviour that we learn from paragraph 2.

(3)

(i) ....

(ii) ....

(iii) ....

2. Why do you think the author uses the phrase "great war" in line 1? **(3)**

....

....

....

....

3. Before line 27, Teddy is only called "the boy".

(a) What effect does the writer create by calling him this? **(2)**

....

....

....

(b) Why do you think this changes in line 27? **(3)**

....

....

....

4. Find two examples of alliteration (repeated consonant sounds). Explain how each one is effective. **(6)**

(i) ....

....

....

(ii) ....

....

....

5.   Explain in your own words:

(a) why it is "the hardest thing in the world to frighten a mongoose" (line 22).

(3)

....

....

....

(b) why Rikki-tikki decides to "stay" (line 40).   **(3)**

....

....

....

6.   Choose two descriptions from the passage, and explain why each one is effective.   **(4)**

(i) ....

....

....

(ii) ....

....

....

7. Based on lines 41-49, what are your impressions of Rikki-tikki's character? Support your points with words and phrases from the passage. **(8)**

....
....
....
....
....
....
....
....
....
....
....
....
....

8. What are the similarities and differences between Teddy's mother and father? Give evidence to support your points. **(8)**

....
....
....
....
....
....
....
....
....
....
....

....

....

....

....

9. What do you imagine Chuchundra the musk-rat (line 3) thinks of Rikki-tikki's behaviour in the passage? Write from Chuchundra's point of view, in the first person (using "I"). Be as creative as you can. **(7)**

....

....

....

....

....

....

....

....

....

....

....

....

....

....

....

....

....

TOTAL MARKS: 50

Blank Page

Rikki-tikki-tavi - Solutions

This comprehension is difficult, because it focuses on explaining information rather than repeating it. It is long, and some of the answers require you to make several points and give evidence. You are expected to understand terms such as "alliteration".

On the other hand, you are given spaces for your answers: these are a useful guide to how much you should write. The last question gives you an opportunity to show off your creative skills.

The Jungle Book is quite different from the Disney film. It is an exciting and beautiful book and well worth reading.

> **1.** **List three things about Rikki-tikki's behaviour that we learn from paragraph 2.** (3)
>
> **(i)** He can "scratch himself anywhere", with any leg.
>
> **(ii)** He can make his tail "fluff up".
>
> **(iii)** He makes a "war cry" that sounds like his name.

I could also have said that his nose is "restless".

Your answers can be short and simple, and it is up to you whether you quote. This question is testing your ability to find information, but also to understand the word "behaviour".

For example, somebody who writes that Rikki-tikki's nose is pink will not get a mark. To say that he is "brave" would be borderline (probably the wrong side of it), because in itself this has more to do with personality than behaviour.

"List" means that you do not have to use full sentences – but you can take this too far! Here is an example of an unclear answer that would only get one mark (achieved for part **(i)**):

> **(i)** *Restless*
>
> **(ii)** *Weasel*
>
> **(iii)** *Cat*

> **2.**   **Why do you think the author uses the phrase "great war" in line 1?**   **(3)**
>
> On the one hand, this phrase suggests the seriousness of what Rikki-tikki will do, implying that his opponents will be a great danger to him. On the other hand, it is ironic: in fact Rikki-tikki is a little animal, not an army, and he will fight "single-handed".

There are various options here, but you are unlikely to find enough to say unless you spot that the phrase is **ironic** ("funny", "humorous" or "surprising", for example, would also be fine). Broadly speaking, two points, at least one of them backed up by an extra explanation, will be likely to get three marks.

An answer that refers to other parts of the passage (for example saying that Rikki-tikki faces lots of risks – such as the bath tub – as you would in a war) could also be acceptable here.

> **3.**   **Before line 27, Teddy is only called "the boy".**
>
> **(a) What effect does the writer create by calling him this?**   **(2)**
>
> Rikki-tikki does not know him: he is just another human. The phrase "the boy" encourages us to see him like this, from Rikki-tikki's point of view.

The word "effect" directs you to think about what this makes the *reader* think or feel. Your point needs to be well explained for two marks. Alternatively, you could make two short points.

> **(b) Why does this change in line 27?**   **(3)**
>
> When Rikki-tikki jumps on Teddy's shoulder, his father says that the mongoose is "making friends". Because Rikki-tikki no longer treats Teddy as a stranger, he no longer sees him as "the boy".

The main point is that the two characters stop being strangers. You must explain why this is, and how you know. Ideally, you should give some evidence: a short quote is the easiest way to do this.

A student wrote this answer, which is also correct:

> This changes because of the dad, who knows the boy's name and presumably says it every day: the author uses "Teddy" once the boy's name has been introduced by his father.

> **4.** **Find two examples of alliteration (repeated consonant sounds). Explain how each one is effective.** **(6)**
>
> **(i)** "Carried him, kicking and clucking" makes me imagine Rikki-tikki's hard, repeated clucking sound when he is scared. It might also sound like the bumping of his body in the flood water.

You need to know what alliteration means: repeated consonant sounds, such as "c, k, c, k," in this case.

Focus on explaining how the sound relates to the meaning.

There is one mark for finding the example, and there are two for explaining its effect. Get the marks easily by making two short points, although one made clearly might well be enough.

> **(ii)** "Fluffed up his fur" creates a fuzzy, soft sound, like the noise of thick fur being brushed. On the other hand, this alliteration could also sound quite grand: Rikki-tikki is proud of his neat new appearance.

Some people give an example of alliteration, but then go wrong by discussing *what the words mean* without talking about the **effect** of their alliterative sounds. Notice how the last part of each sentence in **(ii)** discusses effect.

> **5.** **Explain in your own words:**
>
> **(a) why it is "the hardest thing in the world to frighten a mongoose" (line 22).** **(3)**
>
> This is because every part of him wants to explore things and find out about them. What most animals would see as a threat, he sees as a thing to investigate.

The marks here are for a clear explanation that makes more than one point. The number of marks should tell you this.

It is important to explain the phrase "because he is eaten up from nose to tail with curiosity," using your own words, and to explain why this might make him brave.

> **(b) why Rikki-tikki decides to "stay" (line 40).** **(3)**
>
> There is far more to be learnt in this new place than he could discover at home with his own relatives: he wants to remain so that he learns all he can.

You need to communicate the main ideas from lines 39 and 40, using your own words.

The final part of the example is slightly repetitive, but makes the connection to "staying" completely clear. There probably are not three separate points to be found here: the three marks are for clarity and for showing a full understanding.

> **6.** **Choose two descriptions from the passage, and explain why each one is effective.** (4)
>
> **(i)** "Put his fur in order" suggests that Rikki-tikki has a strong sense of how things ought to be, and great self-respect.

The marks are for the explanation, not for finding the quote (because a description is much easier to find than, for instance, an example of alliteration).

Try to make two short points.

> **(ii)** "Scuttled through the long grass" suggests the quick, secretive way in which the mongoose moves, and also that he is small compared to the grass.

Note that both my examples are descriptions of **actions**. This passage stops to describe the way things look, sound or taste much less often than some others in this pack.

> **7.** **Based on lines 41-49, what are your impressions of Rikki-tikki's character? Support your points with words and phrases from the passage.** (8)
>
> Rikki-tikki is determined, because he spends "all … day" exploring all over the house. He is also a risk-taker, because he goes in the "bath-tubs" and burns himself on a "cigar". He plans his exploration, going to the nursery "to watch how kerosene lamps" work: he likes to think ahead. Finally, he is sociable, because he lies "on the pillow" next to Teddy.

By now you will probably have a good idea of how to answer this sort of question.

"Character" means "personality". You need four different ideas, each backed up with clear evidence (quotes are best).

The easiest way to find your ideas is to **underline** a number of interesting things that Rikki-tikki does, then ask yourself **what kind of person** would do each one. The last step is to choose the four points that are most different from one another.

The most common traps here are:

- to say that he is "curious" or "brave" several times, in different words;
- to talk about his appearance;
- to mention something that he does without explaining what it suggests about his personality.

---

8. **What are the similarities and differences between Teddy's mother and father? Give evidence to support your points.** **(8)**

They are similar because they both like to keep Teddy calm: when he excitedly wants a "funeral" for the mongoose, his mother says "No ... Let's take him in." Later, his father warns Teddy not to "frighten him." Secondly, they both treat animals rather like humans. Teddy's father says that Rikki-tikki is "making friends" and his mother thinks the mongoose is tame because they have been "kind" to him. On the other hand, Teddy's mother likes to be surprised ("and that's a wild creature!"), whereas his father likes to sound serious and knowledgeable ("all mongooses are like that"). Finally, Teddy's mother is cautious: she is worried that Rikki-tikki will "bite the child". His father, on the other hand, is more confident: "He'll do no such thing".

"Similarities" and "differences" are both plural, so strictly speaking you need two of each (with evidence) for eight marks. However, three of one and one of the other would probably also be acceptable.

This question is tricky, because to make a comparison really requires a point about each character: overall, you need eight pieces of evidence. That is a lot of work in an eight mark answer, when you also have to discuss your points.

Therefore, it is particularly important to organise your ideas before you write, underlining your quotes and briefly noting the points that you want to make. This is exactly what I did before writing the answer above.

---

9.   **What do you imagine Chuchundra the musk-rat (line 3) thinks of Rikki-tikki's behaviour in the passage? Write from Chuchundra's point of view, in the first person (using "I"). Be as creative as you can.**   (7)

At first I couldn't believe his arrogance, rushing round the table, even scampering like a ragamuffin over the humans' bodies. I know my place (which is, you must understand, firmly against the skirting-boards): I reckoned a creature like that gave animals a bad name.

I will admit, though – I'm not proud – that I started to come round to his way of thinking. Like an infantry soldier hurling himself towards a line of rifles, he risked life and fur in the pursuit of knowledge. I couldn't even look, as he edged up towards the man's cigar – I, noble Chuchundra of the shadow-bound cupboards and corners, actually flinched (it makes me cringe to admit it) – but when he touched the flame, he hardly squealed. Not half an hour later be was off again in the pursuit of fire. I think it was the lamps, this time.

With the odd word from the wise, here and there along the way, I thought, this strange little being could even make something of himself.

Can you spot how the following information from the passage is suggested in the example above?

*   Rikki-tikki "ran all round the table".
*   He "jumped on the small boy's shoulder" and "climbed up in the big man's lap".
*   Chuchundra "always creeps round by the wall".
*   Rikki-tikki burned his nose "on the end of the big man's cigar".
*   He went "to watch how kerosene lamps were lighted".
*   Chuchundra gave Rikki-tikki "advice, but Rikki-tikki did the real fighting".

This question requires you to imagine Chuchundra's character, based on the information in the first paragraph, and to think about what somebody like this (who is too scared to do things himself, but likes to interfere) would think of Rikki-tikki. You need to "be creative" in the way that you put your ideas together and imagine his character, and of course by using effective language. Notice the use of simile and alliteration in the example, as well as some interesting words such as "ragamuffin" and "pursuit".

If you make more than a couple of English mistakes, you are likely to lose a mark; if you make many, you risk losing two or three.

The example imagines Chuchundra in a way that does not actually fit the rest of Kipling's story very well (in the rest of *Rikki-tikki-tavi* he is less proud, and more timid)

– but that doesn't matter. Comprehension requires you to work with the information in front of you.

END

Paper 8: *The Time Machine*

Type D: Advanced Level

The thought of flight before exploration was even then in my mind. But I said to myself, "You are in for it now," and, feeling my way along the tunnel, I found the noise of machinery grow louder. Presently the walls fell away from me, and I came to a large open space, and striking another match, saw that I had entered a vast arched
5   cavern, which stretched into utter darkness beyond the range of my light. The view I had of it was as much as one could see in the burning of a match.

Necessarily my memory is vague. Great shapes like big machines rose out of the dimness, and cast grotesque black shadows, in which dim spectral Morlocks sheltered from the glare. The place, by the by, was very stuffy and oppressive, and the faint
10   halitus of freshly shed blood was in the air. Some way down the central vista was a little table of white metal, laid with what seemed a meal. The Morlocks at any rate were carnivorous! Even at the time, I remember wondering what large animal could have survived to furnish the red joint I saw. It was all very indistinct: the heavy smell, the big unmeaning shapes, the obscene figures lurking in the shadows, and only
15   waiting for the darkness to come at me again! Then the match burned down, and stung my fingers, and fell, a wriggling red spot in the blackness.

I was afraid to push my way in among all this machinery in the dark, and it was only with my last glimpse of light I discovered that my store of matches had run low. It had never occurred to me until that moment that there was any need to economize
20   them, and I had wasted almost half the box in astonishing the Upper-worlders, to whom fire was a novelty. Now, as I say, I had four left, and while I stood in the dark, a hand touched mine, lank fingers came feeling over my face, and I was sensible of a peculiar unpleasant odour. I fancied I heard the breathing of a crowd of those dreadful little beings about me. I felt the box of matches in my hand being gently disengaged,
25   and other hands behind me plucking at my clothing.

The sense of these unseen creatures examining me was indescribably unpleasant. The sudden realization of my ignorance of their ways of thinking and doing came home to me very vividly in the darkness. I shouted at them as loudly as I could. They started away, and then I could feel them approaching me again. They clutched at me more
30   boldly, whispering odd sounds to each other. I shivered violently, and shouted again—rather discordantly. This time they were not so seriously alarmed, and they made a queer laughing noise as they came back at me. I will confess I was horribly frightened. I determined to strike another match and escape under the protection of its glare. I did so, and eking out the flicker with a scrap of paper from my pocket, I

35   made good my retreat to the narrow tunnel. But I had scarce entered this when my light was blown out and in the blackness I could hear the Morlocks rustling like wind among leaves, and pattering like the rain, as they hurried after me.

From *The Time Machine*, by H. G. Wells

1.   In your own words, write down four facts about the Morlocks.   **(4)**

2.   Copy down a sentence which shows that the narrator (the character who tells the story) may not have remembered everything correctly.   **(1)**

3.   Explain the meaning of the following words, as they are used in the passage:

        (a) grotesque (line 8)   **(2)**

        (b) halitus (line 10)   **(2)**

        (c) disengaged (line 24)   **(2)**

        (d) discordantly (line 31)   **(2)**

4.   Explain why the following descriptions are effective:

        (a) "the walls fell away from me" (line 3)   **(2)**

        (b) "a wriggling red spot in the blackness" (line 16)   **(3)**

        (c) "lank fingers came feeling over my face" (line 22)   **(3)**

5.   What are your impressions of the main character (the narrator)? Give evidence to support your views.   **(8)**

6.   The final sentence contains two similes.

        (a) Write them down.   **(2)**

        (b) Taken together, what is their effect?   **(3)**

7.   How does the author make the passage exciting? Give evidence to support your points.   **(8)**

8.   In your opinion, and giving evidence:

   (a) Where is the passage set?   **(4)**

   (b) Who or what are the Morlocks?   **(4)**

TOTAL MARKS: 50

Blank Page

The Time Machine – Solutions

This is an extremely difficult 11-plus test. You are given no background information, and several of the questions require long, developed answers. What's more, even the shorter questions often require you to be a detective, using clues to reach conclusions. If you do well in this, you already have many of the skills needed for 13-plus.

> **1.   In your own words, write down four facts about the Morlocks.   (4)**
>
> - They eat meat.
> - They live underground.
> - They are smaller than a man.
> - They communicate in their own language.

There are other possibilities, such as "they walk quietly".

This is more difficult than some similar questions you have seen, because the passage does not give you four facts in an obvious way. It is a test of your ability to find (and underline) key information from throughout the text and to work things out (make deductions) from other information. "The Morlocks at any rate were carnivorous" is straightforward – if you know the word "carnivorous". If you don't, the sentences before and after should give you enough clues.

Other facts are mentioned in passing (such as "little beings" and "whispering odd sounds"), but they are spread through the text. You will lose marks if you do not use your own words.

> **2.   Copy down a sentence which shows that the narrator (the character who tells the story) may not have remembered everything correctly.   (1)**
>
> Necessarily my memory is vague.

Don't be tricked by sentences which suggest that it is difficult to *see* things, rather than to remember them.

---

3.   **Explain the meaning of the following words, as they are used in the passage:**

(a) grotesque (line 8) (2)

Distorted, strange, ugly

Any similar meaning. An answer that is plausible (makes sense) but wrong will get one mark.

(b) halitus (line 10) (2)

Breath, or the smell of breath

Anything to do with smell or breath is fine.

This question tests your ability to be calm, even though it is a word that only students of Latin or Italian are likely to know (some other people may know the word "halitosis", meaning "bad breath"). In fact, the rest of the sentence should enable you to work out a meaning that is close enough to get the marks.

(c) disengaged (line 24) (2)

Removed, taken away

Stolen, pulled out, etc.

(d) discordantly (line 31) (2)

With an ugly sound

Anything that implies a clashing sound. This is the hardest word of the four, because there are no good clues.

---

4.   Explain why the following descriptions are effective:

(a) "the walls fell away from me" (line 3)   **(2)**

This helps us imagine the blindness of the narrator: in the darkness, he can only tell that he is entering a cavern because he can't feel the tunnel walls any longer.

(b) "a wriggling red spot in the blackness" (line 16)   **(3)**

This shows us how little light there is in the cavern as the match burns down. "Wriggling" suggests that it is struggling to stay alive – perhaps the character wishes that it would carry on a bit longer. It is only a "spot" because the "blackness" is so deep.

(c) "lank fingers came feeling over my face" (line 22)   **(3)**

This is very sinister. The fingers are bony ("lank") and the narrator is helpless as they "feel" him. Also, the repeated "f" sound (alliteration) is very creepy, because it sounds like the brushing of fingertips.

By this point, you will probably have a good sense of how to explain the effect of quotations. You have to do three things: (i) **separate the different ideas** in the quotation; (ii) explain **their effect on the reader's thoughts/feelings**; (iii) make **enough points** for the number of marks.

---

5.   What are your impressions of the main character (the narrator)? Give evidence to support your views.   **(8)**

The narrator is determined: although he thinks of "flight", he decides to stay because he is "in for it now". He is honest, because he admits that his "memory is vague". He does not always plan things carefully in advance, and he can be wasteful: it had "never occurred" to him not to use up most of his matches. However, when he needs to think quickly, he can be resourceful, as he makes his final match last longer by "eking [it] out" with a "scrap of paper".

This asks specifically for points and for "evidence", so it is likely that the eight marks can be achieved with four such pairings. It would be sensible to find five or six, then choose the best *and most different* four.

I also considered "indescribably unpleasant", which suggests that he hates the feeling of being studied; but I realised that this could be said of most people. Although it might get the marks, it isn't a distinctive feature of *his* character, so it was safer to make a different point.

---

6. **The final sentence contains two similes.**

   (a) Write them down. (2)

"rustling like wind among leaves"; "pattering like the rain"

Even if you have forgotten what a simile is, you can see that this sentence contains the word "like" twice, so this might be a clue.

   (b) Taken together, what is their effect? (3)

They suggest that the Morlocks move very quietly ("rustling") and also that there are many of them ("like the rain"). These images from nature might reflect the narrator's wish to be above ground.

"Taken together" means that you do not need to write a separate answer for each quotation. Indeed, you must make a comment that covers both of them, as in the second sentence of the example.

7. **How does the author make the passage exciting? Give evidence to support your points.** (8)

The reader is only allowed to see what the narrator sees, so shares his sense of mystery and fear. For example, there are "big unmeaning shapes", and figures "lurk" in "shadows". It is hard to be sure whether these things represent a threat, and this uncertainty creates tension. Also exciting is the description of the "red joint" of meat, and its smell in the air. The foreshadowing of "even at the time" implies that there is some secret horror: the reader might wonder whether the Morlocks are eating human flesh. The savagery of this world, with its darkness, raw meat and foul smells, contrasts with the modernity of the "machines" that can be heard ahead, and vaguely seen. This has an unsettling effect, because this underground place is both weird and familiar, which makes it hard to know what to expect. Finally, the text uses different senses to help the reader imagine what it is like to be chased by Morlocks, describing the feel of their "lank fingers" and the sound of their "pattering" feet, so you are worried about whether the narrator will escape.

This sort of question is at the most difficult extreme of 11-plus work: it would be more typical of a 13-plus paper.

The crucial thing is to focus on **how the story affects the reader**. Look for **points when the main character experiences strong emotions**, and ask yourself **how the author helps you to feel similar things**.

Four points, explained with evidence, make a perfect answer.

It is possible that fewer points, well explained, could also achieve eight marks. For example, the first point above (from "The reader" to "tension") is so thoroughly developed that it might be worth three. However, you should try to write safe answers whenever you have enough time to do so, which in this case would mean four points with evidence.

> **8.   In your opinion, and giving evidence:**
>
> **(a) Where is the passage set?**   **(4)**
>
> The passage is set deep underground, because the narrator travels through a "tunnel" and enters "a vast arched cavern". It is probably also set on another planet and/or in a different time, because there do not seem to be any "large animals" to eat. A different time is more likely, because of the title, "The Time Machine".

Two points, explained with evidence, are needed. They need to make sense in the light of the whole passage. You do not need to know the rest of H.G. Wells' book!

In fact, it is set in England in the distant future, but an argument that (for example) it is set on another planet could just as well achieve the marks.

> **(b) Who or what are the Morlocks?**   **(4)**
>
> The Morlocks do not seem like any creature that I have heard of: they are intelligent enough to operate "machines", but are tiny with strange, "lank" fingers. I think they are a sort of ape that has become very intelligent: they are small, shuffling things, but they eat from a "table" and have a language of their own ('whispering odd sounds to each other").

This is similar to part **(a)**, although one main point (in the example, that they are a sort of evolved ape), explained with several supporting ideas and with evidence, should be sufficient.

In fact, the Morlocks are humans who have evolved to live underground: they eat less intelligent people from the surface.

END
